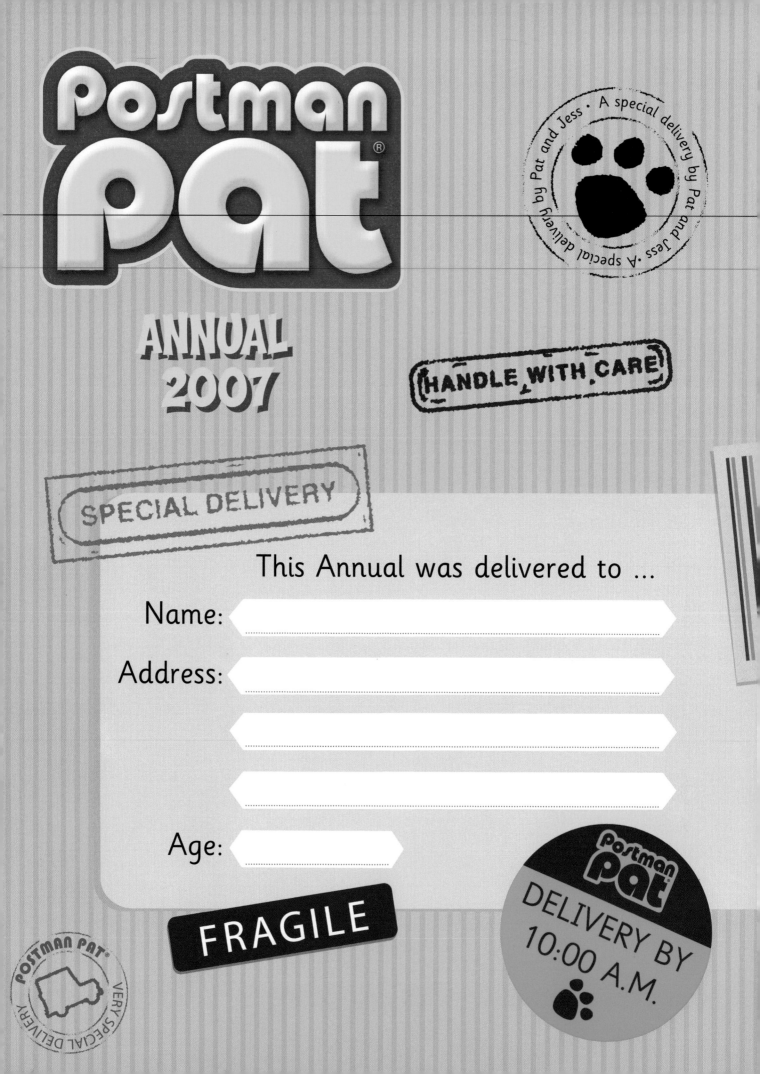

Contents

EGMONT

We bring stories to life

First published in Great Britain 2006 by Egmont UK Limited
239 Kensington High Street, London W8 6SA

Written and edited by Brenda Apsley
Designed by Graham Wise

Stories adapted from original scripts by Gillian Corderoy and Diane Redmond.

ISBN 978 1 4052 2617 2
ISBN 1 4052 2617 X
10 9 8 7 6 5 4 3 2 1
Printed in Italy

Hello!

I hope you enjoy my new annual!
You can read about **Mrs Goggins'** special ride,
Doctor Gilbertson's birthday surprise
– and the day when I delivered
the post on **roller-blades!**

All About the Clifton Family

Pat Clifton is the Greendale village postman and it's his job to make sure that all his friends and neighbours get their cards, letters and parcels every day.

Everyone knows Pat and his red van. Greendale is a friendly place and Pat loves meeting lots of people.

Pat lives on the edge of the village in a house called Forge Cottage.

Jess is Pat's black and white cat and goes everywhere with him, on the passenger seat of his van.

Jess loves eating fish, chasing mice — and sleeping. He's always poking his little pink nose into all sorts of things!

Royal
E㼤R Mail

PAT 1

Can you find these names in the letter puzzle? They are spelled out from top to bottom and from left to right.

JESS   PAT

JULIAN   SARA

A	J	E	S	S
C	U	B	A	X
K	L	L	R	O
G	I	M	A	D
P	A	T	E	H
F	N	R	T	J

Post Office

Sara Clifton is Pat's wife. She makes lovely cakes, so working in the Greendale Light Railway station café is the perfect job for her!

Julian Clifton is Sara and Pat's son. He's mad about football and likes going to Pencaster United matches with his dad.

9

All About Greendale

Greendale is a friendly little village. There's a church, a school, a village green, lots of farms and houses – and the Post Office, of course.

PC Arthur Selby is the Greendale policeman. He looks after things and makes sure the roads are safe. He rides around on a big black bicycle.

Mrs Goggins looks after the Post Office in the High Street. She sorts out the post for Pat to deliver and has a little white dog called Bonnie.

Ted Glen is the Greendale handyman. If anything gets broken, he'll fix it. He helps at the railway, and lives at the Watermill.

Colour in the pictures of **Mrs Goggins, Ted Glen** and **Reverend Timms.**

Julia Pottage lives at Greendale Farm. She has a herd of dairy cows for milk, and lots and lots of sheep.

Doctor Sylvia Gilbertson works at the clinic in Greendale. She works hard making sure everyone stays fit and healthy.

Reverend Peter Timms is the Greendale Vicar. He lives in a house next door to his church. Everyone likes him because he's kind and fun.

Alf Thompson has a small farm called Thompson Ground. He grows vegetables and keeps pigs, hens and chickens.

Dorothy Thompson works with her husband, Alf. She makes cheese from their goats' milk and sells it at Pencaster Market.

11

All About Julian and His Friends

Greendale Primary is the village school. It's friendly and has just one teacher.

Jeff Pringle is the teacher at Greendale Primary. He always tries to make his lessons fun.

Charlie Pringle is Mr Pringle's son. He's seven years old and his favourite lesson is science. He loves playing on his computer.

Tom Pottage is Katy's twin brother. He doesn't mind being the youngest. He likes looking after their pet sheep, Parsley and Sage.

Julian Clifton is six years old. He likes school — but not as much as playing sports! He likes the countryside, too — and Jess!

Katy Pottage is six years old and lives at Greendale Farm with her mum and twin brother. She's a few minutes older than him and can be a bit bossy.

Can you answer these questions about Julian and his friends?

1) How old is Bill Thompson?

2) Who likes playing sports?

3) Who used to be Julian's pen friend?

4) Whose dad is a policeman?

5) What is Mr Pringle's son called?

Bill Thompson is nine years old. He lives at Thompson Ground, his family's farm. When he grows up he wants to be a farmer, just like his dad!

Lucy Selby is seven years old and her dad is the village policeman. She likes dressing up and playing let's-pretend games and reading.

Meera Bains is seven. She was Julian's pen friend until she moved to Greendale. Now she's his **real** friend!

Sarah Gilbertson is eight years old and her mum is the Greendale doctor. She loves chatting and asking questions.

ANSWERS: 1) Nine, 2) Julian, 3) Meera, 4) Lucy, 5) Charlie.

All About the Bains Family

Ajay Bains is the Greendale Light Railway stationmaster and he drives the train. He makes sure the station is clean and tidy and that the Greendale Rocket runs on time to and from Pencaster.

GRE...ALE

G.R.

The **Greendale Rocket** is the name of the old steam engine that pulls the train between Greendale and Pencaster. It has a carriage for passengers and a bright red mail van at the back.

Who is riding in the Greendale Rocket with Ajay?

Use this little picture to help you colour in the Greendale Rocket below.

Nisha Bains is Ajay's wife. She has two jobs at the railway. She sells tickets and serves in the station café with Sara. The café is the perfect place to stop for a cup of tea – and one of Sara's cakes.

Nikhil Bains is the baby of the family. He's just six months old and is a really happy baby who is always smiling. Most people call him Nik.

GREENDALE

Here's **Meera Bains** again! She is Ajay and Nisha's daughter.

ANSWER: Pat and Jess are riding in the Greendale Rocket.

Postman Pat and the Big Balloon Ride

The streets were covered in snow when Pat arrived at the Post Office, one cold January morning.

Mrs Goggins was looking at a magazine with hot-air balloons on the cover. "What an adventure a balloon ride would be," said Mrs Goggins.

Later, Pat drove to Ted Glen's House with the post. Ted was shovelling snow. When he tossed some over his shoulder, it landed – **SPLAT!** – on Pat, giving him a white snowy beard!

Pat gave Ted his post then asked, "Have you still got that old hot-air balloon, Ted?"

"Yes," said Ted. "What do you want it for?"

"We're going to take Mrs Goggins ballooning!" said Pat.

They put the balloon into Pat's van and drove to the village green.

"Right," said Ted, turning on the air bottle. "Let's get it blown up."

The balloon began to fill up then — **hiss!** — Pat heard a noise. "What's that?" he asked.

Hisss! "It's sprung a leak," said Ted.

HISSSSS! Even more air escaped and the balloon collapsed — on Pat!

"I'll fix it while you go and get Mrs Goggins," said Ted.

When Pat got to the Post Office, he led Mrs Goggins outside. "Close your eyes," he said.

"Where are you taking me?" she asked.

"It's a surprise!" said Pat.

At Greendale Primary, Mr Pringle was telling the children about Nature Trail Day. "Have you got your lists?" he asked. "Let's see how many different flowers and animals we can find."

Later, they were out in the fields ticking the flowers on their lists, when Julian heard a noise coming from a bush. It was a little white dog!

"**Dog** isn't on the list," said Charlie.

"But it **is** an animal, so we'll write it down anyway!" said Mr Pringle.

"I wonder what it's called?" said Julian.

Back in Greendale, Ted had fixed the balloon when PC Selby arrived. "Have you seen a little white dog, Ted?" he asked. "It's a stray. I've got to take it to the Dogs' Home. I'll let you park this balloon here if you help me find it."

"All right, Arthur," said Ted, walking towards the church. "But let's hurry. **Here, Doggie**!"

When Pat arrived with Mrs Goggins, she couldn't believe her eyes. "Oh, the balloon's lovely!" she said. "Are you going to fly it?"

"No, we'll wait for Ted," said Pat. "I wonder where he's gone?"

While they were waiting for Ted, Mrs Goggins and Pat climbed into the basket to see what it was like. "What's this?" asked Mrs Goggins, touching the air control.

Just then, Jess tried to jump into the basket but he missed and tripped on a rope tied to a metal ring.

The rope was what was keeping the balloon on the ground! It came undone and the balloon started to rise into the air! "Oh, no!" said Pat. "We're flying!"

"Meow!" said Jess, climbing in.

The balloon floated off over the snowy rooftops. It went higher and higher.

"Oooooh!" said Pat and Mrs Goggins. **"Meooooow!"** said Jess.

Out in the fields, Charlie was using his binoculars to look for birds. "I've found one!" he said. "It's round and red with yellow stripes. It's a ..."

"Hot-air balloon!" cried the others as the balloon floated over them with Mrs Goggins at the controls.

On their way back to school, the children met Ted and PC Selby.

"Here's my missing dog!" said PC Selby.

"And there's my balloon!" said Ted. "Over here, Mrs Goggins! Let some more air out and we'll grab the rope!"

The balloon floated down and the little dog grabbed the rope in its teeth.

"Well done, Mrs Goggins," said Ted. "I couldn't have flown it better myself!"

When Mrs Goggins saw the little dog she asked who she belonged to. PC Selby told her she was a stray.

"That's a shame," said Mrs Goggins. "Can I keep her?"

PC Selby smiled and nodded.

Julian asked, "What are you going to call her?"

"Well, I've had a bonnie day," said Mrs Goggins. "So I'll call her — **Bonnie**!"

Pat's Quiz

Did you enjoy the hot-air balloon story? Try and answer these questions about it!

1. What month of year was it when Greendale was covered in snow?

2. Who used his binoculars to look for birds?

3. The hot-air balloon was red and green.

true or false

☐ ☐

4. Who took the children on a Nature Trail Day?

5. Here's Julian setting off with three of his friends, Charlie, Bill – and who else?

How many children can you count in this picture?

---

7. What name did Mrs Goggins give her new dog? Was it:
a) Bobby
b) Bonnie or
c) Bossy?

8. Who did the hot-air balloon belong to? Was it:
a) Ted Glen
b) Mrs Goggins or
c) PC Selby?

9. PC Selby was looking for a stray cat.

true   or   false

☐   ☐

10. Who did Ted tell to "Let some more air out!"?

ANSWERS: 1. January, 2. Charlie, 3. False, 4. Mr Pringle, 5. Meera, 6. Eight children, 7. b, Bonnie, 8. a, Ted Glen, 9. False, he was looking for a dog, 10. Mrs Goggins.

23

Big Pictures, Little Pictures

Which of the little pictures can you see in the big ones?
Write a tick ✔ for the ones you can see.

1

a.

b.

c.

d.

24

Postman Pat and the Surprise Present

Pat was just finishing his round when he saw Doctor Gilbertson walking along the lane. "What are you doing so far from home?" he asked.

"I'm on my way to see Alf," said Doctor Gilbertson. "He's in bed with a bad cold."

Pat gave the doctor a lift. "It must be hard, visiting patients without a car," he said.

"Yes, but home visits are part of my job," said Doctor Gilbertson. "They have to be done."

Pat had a card for Doctor Gilbertson.

"It's a birthday card from my sister," she said.

"I hope you've got something special planned?" said Pat.

"Oh, no, I'm too **busy** for birthdays," said Doctor Gilbertson. "Thanks for the lift, Pat."

Later on, Charlie and Julian met Sarah Gilbertson. "It's Mum's birthday," she told them. "I want to do something special but I can't think of anything."

"I've got an idea," said Charlie. "We'll write a song for her!"

When Pat took some post to Ted Glen, he told him about Doctor Gilbertson having to do her visits on foot.

"She needs something to help her get around," said Ted.

"Rollerskates?

A bicycle?

A skateboard?"

"What she needs is a **car**," said Pat.

"A car, eh?" said Ted, showing Pat an old sports car. "There's just one problem. This car hasn't started in years."

Ted was trying to fix the car, when PC Selby arrived. "You need an expert with engines," he said. "Ajay!"

Pat rang Ajay in the station café, who said he'd help. Then Ajay told Nisha and Sara about Doctor Gilbertson's birthday.

"We'll give her a surprise tea-party as well as the car!" said Nisha.

Later, Ajay was working on the car when Ted brought a bucket of soapy water to clean it. But he tripped over Jess ... the water slopped out ... and PC Selby was soaked!

"MEOW!" Poor Jess got wet as well!

As Ajay worked, PC Selby polished the hub caps and Pat cleaned the seats.

But Jess was much more interested in the exhaust pipe. He put his face up close to it and looked inside, just as Ajay said, "She's finished!" and Ted started the engine. All that happened was that black smoke puffed out of the pipe all over Jess!

"Meow!" said Jess.

But he wouldn't leave the pipe alone, and touched it with his paw.

PC Selby shone his torch into the pipe. "There's the problem," he said, pulling out an old mouse's nest.

"No wonder the car wouldn't go," said Ted.

Ajay soon got the car started. **"Bingo!"** he said.

Back in Greendale, Doctor Gilbertson went to Forge Cottage with a jar of jam as a thank you for Pat. But there was no one in so she sat down on the swing seat in the garden to wait. Soon, she was fast asleep.

While she slept, Sara and Nisha got the party ready.

But where was Doctor Gilbertson? "I can't find her," said Pat.

Pat didn't know where she was – but Jess did! She was still asleep on the swing seat.

"**Meow!**" said Jess. "**MEOW!**"

Doctor Gilbertson woke up and walked to the village green with Jess.

As they arrived the party began. The children sang a special song and Sarah gave her mum a big hug. "Happy birthday, Mum," she said.

"Oh, thank you!" said Doctor Gilbertson.

Just then, Ajay and Ted arrived in the sports car. "Do you like it, Doctor?" said Ted.

"It's beautiful," said Doctor Gilbertson.

"Good," said Ajay. "Because it's for you!"

"I don't know what to say!" said Doctor Gilbertson.

"There's only one thing **to** say," said Pat. "**Happy Birthday!**"

Read with Postman Pat

Can you read the story with me? When you see a picture, say the name.

Poor  had to walk to visit her patients because she didn't have a car.  wanted to give  a car for her birthday.  had an old car but it wouldn't go.  and  and  couldn't fix it, so they asked  to help.

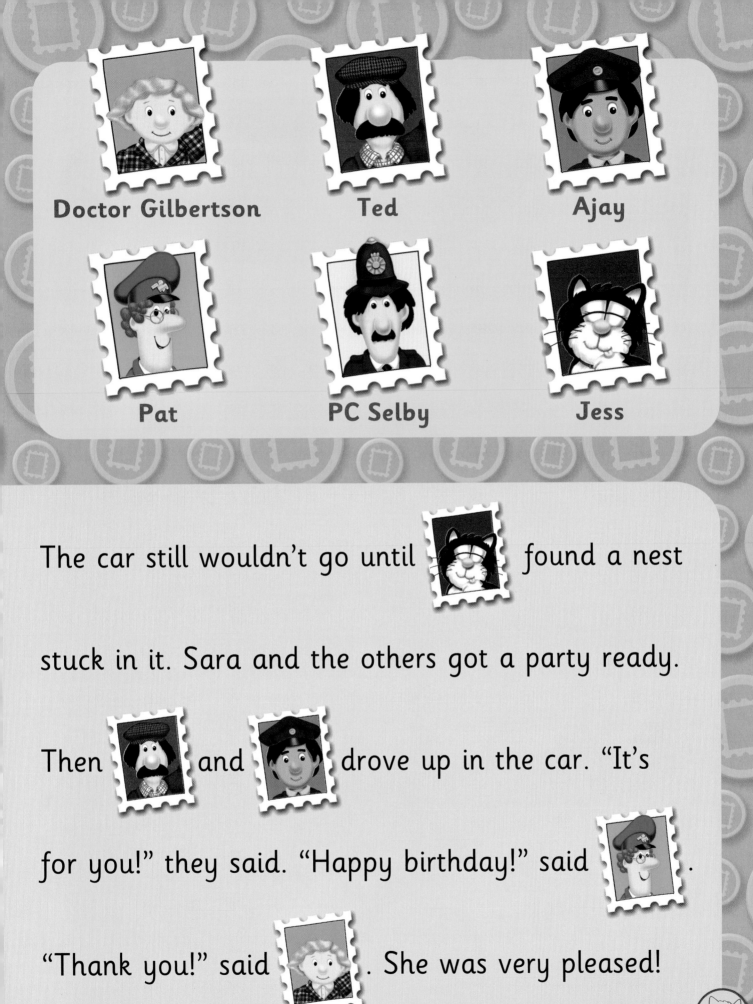

Doctor Gilbertson

Ted

Ajay

Pat

PC Selby

Jess

The car still wouldn't go until found a nest

stuck in it. Sara and the others got a party ready.

Then and drove up in the car. "It's

for you!" they said. "Happy birthday!" said .

"Thank you!" said . She was very pleased!

Surprise Presents

Julian got a train set.

Tom and **Katy** got a see-saw.

Meera got a doll and a pushchair.

Charlie got a kite.

Jess got a birthday surprise too – a BIG saucer of milk!

Can you answer these questions about the surprise presents?

a) Who got a **kite**?

b) What did **Tom** and **Katy** get?

c) Who got a **doll** and a pushchair?

Postman Pat and the Perfect Pizza

It was a windy day in Greendale. Pat gave Julian a lift to school because he was taking a tree for Tree Planting Day.
"We've got five trees already," Bill told Pat when they got

to Greendale Primary. "Six with Julian's."

"And when we've planted them, Dad's making pizza for everyone," said Meera. "He's using Mrs Pottage's oven."

Later on, Pat drove to Greendale Farm to see how Ajay was getting on.

Ajay was unloading things from his motorbike. "Thanks for babysitting Nikhil, Julia," he said.

"No problem," said Julia. "What are you putting on the pizzas?"

"I've got a special recipe for the **perfect pizza**!" said Ajay.

Just then, Pat arrived. "How are the pizzas going?" he asked. "The children are going to be really hungry after all that tree-planting."

"Oh, no! The trees! I forgot all about them," said Julia. "I said I'd take them to school for the twins."

"Don't worry," said Ajay. "Leave Nikhil with me."

"And I'll give you a hand, Ajay," said Pat.

"Right," said Ajay. "I'll mix the dough, then we'll make the bases."

The children were digging holes for their trees when Charlie's glasses fell off and down a hole.

"If they get buried, no one will find them for years and years," said Bill.

"You've given me an idea, Bill," said Mr Pringle. "What if you all find something special from Greendale and bury it under your tree? When people find the things in years to come they'll know something about our village."

"A **map**!" said Sarah.

"A **picture** of my dad!" said Lucy.

"A **maths book**," said Charlie.

"Great ideas!" said Mr Pringle. "Go and find your things and we'll meet back here, later."

The children all found special things to bury — except Julian and Meera. They just couldn't decide what to bury.

Back at Greendale Farm, Ajay and Pat had made the pizza dough. "You have to spin it around, like this," said Ajay. He spun his dough but it flew out of his hand and stuck to the ceiling – then it fell down on to Pat's head!

When Pat spun his dough, it landed on Ajay!

Pat and Ajay made the bases then added the toppings. "**Mushrooms, peppers**," said Pat. "And **cheese** and ..."

"**Pineapple**!" said Ajay. "That's what makes it my extra-special recipe."

Soon, all the pizzas were ready. "Mmm, they smell good," said Pat.

"Let's get them to the school while they're still hot," said Ajay.

Pat put the pizzas into boxes and loaded them into his van. Then he set off with Jess and Nikhil, while Ajay tidied up.

But Pat didn't get far. The wind had blown down a tree and it was blocking the lane to Greendale!

Pat went back to tell Ajay. "How are we going to get the pizzas to the school?" asked Ajay.

Pat had an idea. "I'll take them on your motorbike," he said. "Across the fields!"

They put the pizza boxes in the sidecar with Jess on top, then Pat set off. The wind was still blowing hard and the stack of pizzas began to wobble.

"Hang on!" said Pat.

"Meow!" said Jess.

Pat got back on the road at last. All the children cheered and clapped when he got to the school.

"Somebody order a pizza?" said Pat.

The children loved Ajay's pizzas. Pat said, "Three cheers for the pizza chef! **Hip, hip, hurray**!" when Ajay arrived.

Now Julian and Meera knew what they were going to bury under their tree – Ajay's special recipe for **perfect pineapple pizza**!

Count with Pat

Julian and Meera couldn't decide what to bury under their tree. They got all their toys out to see if they could find something.

Colour in the number of different balls you can see in the picture then count them, and write the number of each colour.

Dad and Jess had a **LOT** of pizza boxes to take to school!
Whoa! Jess nearly fell off!

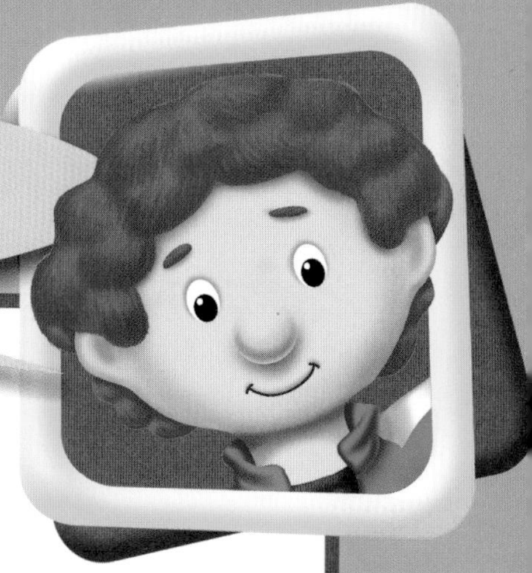

Draw and colour in a pizza for each box you can see in the big picture below.

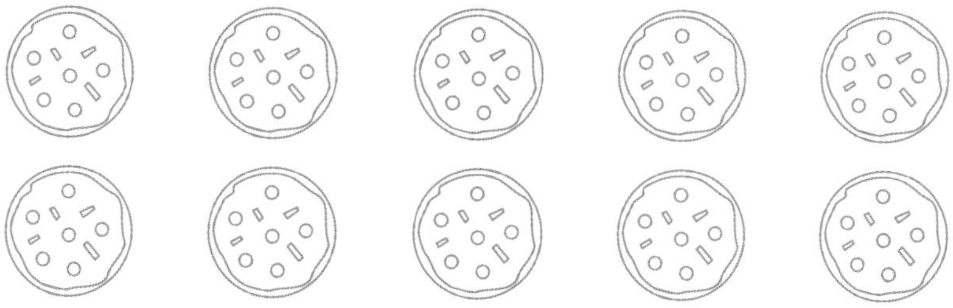

Now count the pizzas. How many did Pat and Jess deliver? Circle the right number.

1 2 3 4 5 6 7 8 9 10

ANSWERS: There are 3 red balls, 3 pink balls, 1 blue ball and 1 yellow ball. Pat and Jess delivered 9 pizzas.

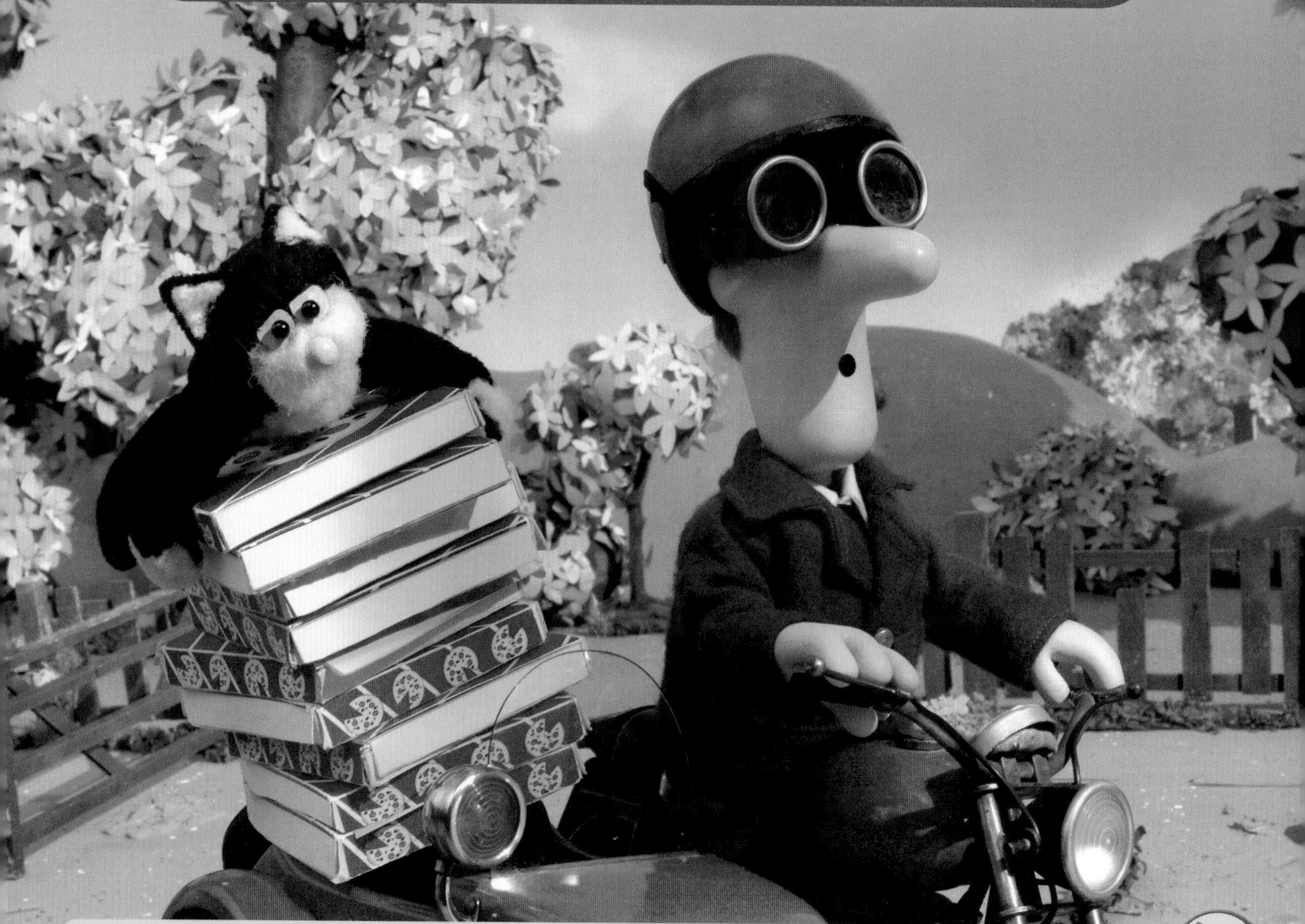

Postman Pat and the Pet Show

One morning, Julian was telling his mum and dad about the Greendale Pet Show. It was going to be held on the village green.

"Who are you taking?" Postman Pat asked Julian.

"Jess, of course!" said Julian.

When Julian met Sarah Gilbertson, he asked her which pet she was taking to the show.

"I haven't got a pet to take!" said Sarah. "It's not fair!"

Just then, Jess appeared. "There's Jess," said Julian.
Sarah smiled. "You'll let me take **Jess** to the
show?" she said.

"What?" said Julian. He didn't know what
to say! "Er ... I didn't mean ..."

Sarah grabbed Jess and walked off with him.
"Thanks, Julian!" she said.

When Julian caught up with Sarah, she was trying to train Jess like a dog!

"Sit!" said Sarah.

"Meow!" said Jess, walking away.

"Cats aren't like dogs," Julian told her. "They don't do tricks."

"He'll learn!" said Sarah. "After I've tidied him up."

"Jess doesn't like being combed," said Julian.

But Sarah took no notice. "He's got to be a pretty pussycat for the show," she said.

Jess took one look at the comb and ribbon she was holding and ran off.

"Come back!" said Sarah.

Jess ran to the school where Mr Pringle and Charlie were trying to catch Dotty, the guinea pig.

"Squeak!" said Dotty.

"Meow!" said Jess.

Dotty took one look at Jess and scampered back into her cage.

"Thanks, Jess," said Charlie. "We'd never have caught her without your help."

Just then, Jess heard a voice he didn't like.

"Jess!" called Sarah. "Where are you?"

"Meow!" said Jess, and he ran off again.

Tom and Katy Pottage were trying to catch their sheep, Parsley and Sage, when Jess arrived at Greendale Farm.

"Baaaaa!" said the sheep.

"Meow!" said Jess, scampering towards them.

The sheep took one look at Jess and ran into their pen.

"Thanks, Jess!" said Tom.

Back in the village Julian told Pat about Jess. "We've lost him, Dad!" he said.

"Don't worry," said Pat. "We'll look for him in the van."

When Jess got back to the village, he met Meera and Mrs Goggins' dog, Bonnie. "We've lost Bonnie's ball," Meera told him, as Jess heard a voice he didn't like ...

"Jess!" called Sarah.

Jess ran off and hid behind a barrel of flowers until Sarah had gone. When he came out again, he had Bonnie's ball in his mouth. "Thank you, Jess!" said Meera.

Pat and Julian looked for Jess all over the village but he was nowhere to be seen. "Let's try the village green," said Pat.

When they got there, Mr Pringle was reading out the names of the pets in the show. "There's Blob the goldfish," he said, "and ..."

"Jess!" said Julian, as Jess jumped into his arms.

Jess purred happily and Sarah saw how happy he looked with Julian. "Jess is your pet, Julian," she said. "You enter him in the show."

Soon the show was over. "All the animals win a prize," said Mr Pringle. "But there's a special prize for ... Jess! Without his help Charlie wouldn't have caught Dotty."

"And we wouldn't have caught Parsley and Sage," said Tom.

"And Bonnie would never have found her ball," said Meera.

"Jess gets a special prize for being such a clever, helpful pet," said Mr Pringle, and everyone cheered.

"MEOW!" said Jess happily.

49

Pat's Quiz

Did you like the Pet Show story?
Answer these questions
about it, then try the puzzle.

1. Who didn't have a pet to take to the Pet Show?

2. What is the name of Charlie Pringle's guinea pig? Is it:
a) Lotty
b) Dotty or
c) Potty?

3. This is Jess saying hello to Blob the goldfish and his owner. Whose pet is he?

4. Meera Bains owns Bonnie the dog. **true** or false?

5. What colour is Bonnie?

6. Who gave out the prizes at the Pet Show. Was it:
a) Reverend Timms
b) Mr Pringle or
c) Postman Pat?

7. Jess helped round up Tom and Katy's sheep. What are their names?

50

8. What did Jess find when he hid behind a barrel?

9. Which pet won a special prize for being helpful?

10. These pictures are of Julian telling his mum and dad about the Greendale Pet Show. They look the same, but there are 5 things that are different in picture 2. Can you spot the differences?

ANSWERS: 1. Sarah Gilbertson, 2. b) Dotty, 3. Lucy Selby's, 4. False, she belongs to Mrs Goggins, 5. White; 6. b) Mr Pringle, 7. Parsley and Sage, 8. Bonnie's ball, 9. Jess, 10. Lampshade has changed colour, Pat's buttons are missing, stripes are missing from Julian's trainers, the hands on the clock have moved, flowers have disappeared.

Postman Pat and the Thunderstorm

It was a dark autumn day in Greendale. "I think there's a thunderstorm coming," Pat told Mrs Goggins.

"I hope not," said Mrs Goggins. "I have to take Bonnie for her walk soon. She's got a new toy bone and won't go anywhere without it."

Suddenly, there was a distant clap of thunder. Bonnie

shivered and shook. "Don't worry, Bonnie," said Pat.
"Come on Jess, let's get home before the rain starts."
Mrs Goggins decided to take Bonnie for her
walk before the storm came. She couldn't find
her squeaky bone toy anywhere and had to
go without it.

When Pat got home, Julian and Meera were playing superheroes in the garden.

"Help!" cried Meera.

"This is a job for **Captain Zap!**" said Julian.

"What are you two up to?" asked Pat.

"We're the **bravest** superheroes in the world," said Julian.

Just then, a big **rumble** of thunder filled the air and the sky got darker.

"Come inside or you'll be the **wettest** superheroes," said Pat. "There's a storm coming."

Then Meera saw something in Jess' mouth. He had taken Bonnie's toy bone!

"Oh, you naughty cat," said Pat as lightning flashed and the rain started. "We can't take it back now. Come on, inside!"

Mrs Goggins and Bonnie were out on their walk when the storm came. There was a big **clap** of thunder and a **flash** of lightning. Mrs Goggins dropped Bonnie's lead and Bonnie ran away! "Come back!" cried Mrs Goggins.

Safe and dry at Forge Cottage, Meera wanted to carry on playing superheroes. But where was Julian?

She found him in his bedroom with the covers over his head! He didn't like the storm and was shaking with fear.

Pat explained that thunderstorms were just electricity in the sky. "But that doesn't stop me being scared," said Julian. "I'll **never** be a superhero. They're not scared of anything!"

"Being brave means doing something even though you're scared," said Sara.

Just then, Mrs Goggins arrived. She was very wet – and very worried.

"Bonnie ran away when she heard the thunder," she said. "We were **so** scared."

"Don't worry, I'll find her," said Pat.

"Oh, thank you, Pat, thank you," said Mrs Goggins.

"Can I come with you, Dad?" asked Julian.

"But aren't you scared of the storm?" said Pat.

"Being brave means doing something even if you're scared. Right, Mum?"

"Right!" said Sara.

"Come on, then, Captain Zap," said Pat. "Let's find that puppy!"

Pat drove to Thompson Ground. He thought Bonnie might be hiding in the barn. But Bonnie wasn't there. "Why don't you try Greendale Farm?" Alf suggested.

Bonnie wasn't there either. "How about the railway bridge?" said Julia.

On the way the van got stuck in a big puddle of water, and Pat and Julian had to walk across the dark fields. "Here, Bonnie!" they called.

Suddenly, they heard a whimper!

"Come on!" said Julian. "Follow the noise!"

When Pat and Julian got to the railway bridge Bonnie peeped out from a hole in the wall where she had been hiding. "Let's take you home," said Pat.

But Bonnie was still scared and disappeared back into the hole.

"We need something to make her come out," said Julian. "I know! Her squeaky bone! I'll stay with her while you get it."

Pat fetched Bonnie's toy bone. As soon as she heard its squeak, she came out of the hole and jumped into Julian's arms.

"How can I ever thank you, Pat?" said Mrs Goggins when they got back to Forge Cottage.

"It was Julian who had the idea of using the toy," said Pat. "And Julian who stayed with Bonnie in the storm."

"You're a real hero, Julian," said Mrs Goggins.

"You did something very brave even though you were scared," said Meera.

"And that makes you a **SUPERHERO**!" said Pat.

Read with Postman Pat

Can you read the story with me? When you see a picture, say the name.

Poor  was scared of the storm and

ran away to hide. was scared, too.

found him hiding under the covers.

told that he would find .

asked if he could go with him.

58

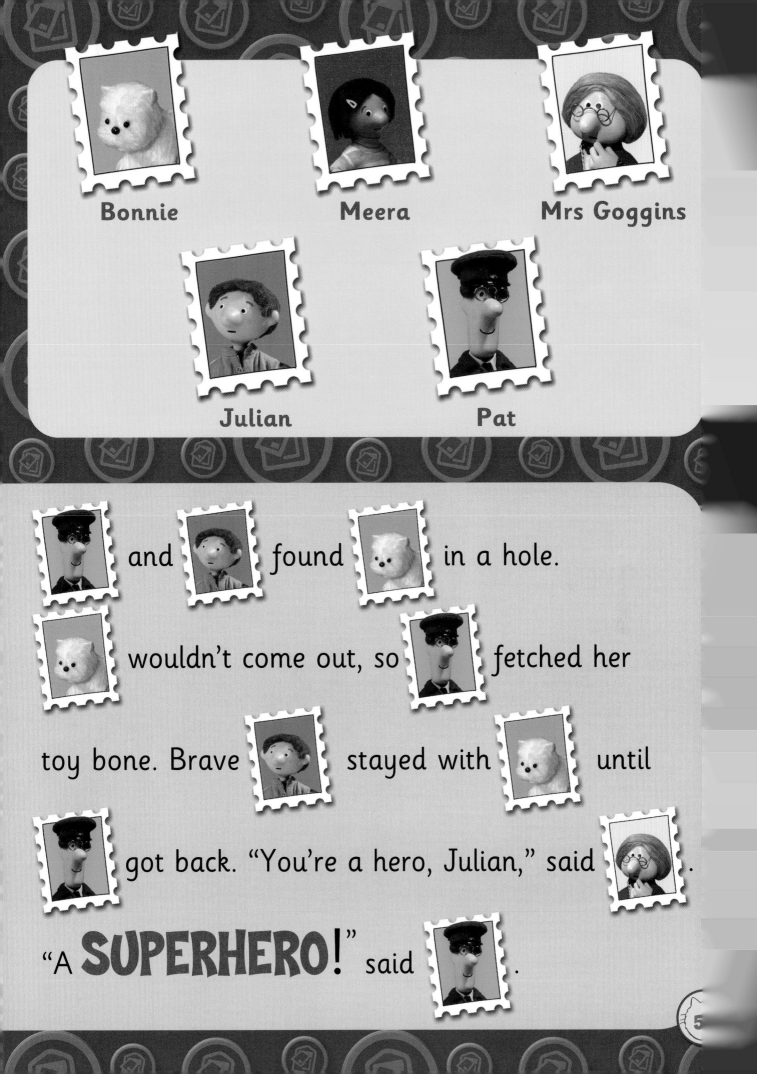

Bonnie

Meera

Mrs Goggins

Julian

Pat

and found in a hole.

wouldn't come out, so fetched her

toy bone. Brave stayed with until

got back. "You're a hero, Julian," said .

"A **SUPERHERO!**" said .

5

Pat's Jigsaw Picture Puzzles

Can you find the two pieces that will fit into the
spaces to complete each jigsaw picture?
You can draw and colour in the pieces if you like.

a.

b.

c.

d.

e.

60

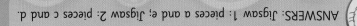
ANSWERS: Jigsaw 1: pieces a and e; Jigsaw 2: pieces c and d.

Postman Pat and the Tricky Transport Day

It was winter in Greendale – and it was snowing!

"Can we make a snowman, Dad?" asked Julian.

"You make a start and I'll help you after work," said Pat.

Pat set off in his van. He hadn't gone far when the engine made a funny noise. "That doesn't sound right," said Pat.

He drove to Ted's house. "Can you mend it, Ted?" asked Pat.
"Aye," said Ted. "But it'll take all day."
"Oh, no," said Pat. "It'll take ages to deliver the post on foot."
"You can borrow my **truck**," said Ted.
"Thanks, Ted," said Pat. "I will."

Pat and Jess set off in Ted's truck but by the time they got to Alf's yard, it had started making a funny noise, as well!

"My van isn't working so Ted said I could use his truck," Pat told Alf. "Now it's broken down, too."

"Borrow my **tractor** then," said Alf.

Pat and Jess rode to Greendale Station on Alf's tractor, but when Pat got back on after delivering the post the engine wouldn't start!

"Got a problem, Pat?" called Ajay as he puffed into the station on the Greendale Rocket.

"My van's broken down," said Pat. "Ted's mending it so I'm using Alf's tractor, but now it won't start."

"I can lend you my **motorbike**," said Ajay.

"But what about Jess?" said Pat.

"Follow me," said Ajay.

Ajay took them to the engine shed and wheeled out his motorbike. "Jess can ride in the sidecar!" said Ajay.

Pat put on Ajay's crash helmet and goggles, and Jess jumped into the sidecar. Then they set off to deliver the rest of the post.

Pat was riding along by the railway line when – **hiss!** – he got a puncture and the tyre went flat. "Oh, no!" said Pat, but then he heard a whistle. "It's the Rocket!" he said, waving his arms around. "Stop, Ajay, **stop**!"

Ajay put on the brakes and leant out of the cab.

"Sorry, Ajay," said Pat. "The bike's got a puncture. Can you take me somewhere near Greendale Farm?"

"Course I can," said Ajay. "Climb on board."

Ajay dropped Pat and Jess at a little station out in the country. "Thanks, Ajay," said Pat.

They were still a long way from Greendale Farm and it was hard work walking through the thick snow.

Pat was soon out of breath and stopped for a rest. Just then, Meera, Bill and Charlie arrived with their sledges.

"What's wrong, Pat?" asked Bill.

"I've got to take the post to Greendale Farm and I'm late," said Pat.

"Take my **sledge**," said Bill. "It's fast."

"Thanks, Bill," said Pat. "Hop on, Jess!"

Pat and Jess set off down the hill to the farm. But the snow was very slippery and the sledge went fast, **very** fast.

"**Oooo!**" said Pat. "Help!"

"**Meow!**" said Jess.

Pat steered the sledge into Julia's yard but he didn't know how to stop it. Suddenly, they crashed into a pile of hay bales!

Poor Jess flew into the air and landed in Julia's laundry basket!

"**MEOW!**" said Jess.

Pat gave Julia her post. But there was still one letter in his bag. "Oh, no," said Pat. "It's for Ted! How am I going to get to him?"

"You can skate there on my **roller-blades**," said Tom.

Pat put on the skates and Jess jumped up on to his back then they **wibble-wobbled** down the lane.

"Oooo!" said Pat, trying not to lose his balance. **"Aaaaaah!"**

"Meow!" said Jess.

When Pat got to the road he couldn't stop and he and Jess fell into a big pile of snow!

"You'd better come in the car with me, Pat," said PC Selby.

By the time they got to Ted's yard, the van was fixed and Pat drove home. He wanted to see Julian's snowman.

But Julian hadn't made a snowman. "Whoo-whoo!" said Julian. "It's a snow **train**!"

Jess was watching when some snow fell from the shed roof. Then a bigger lump fell, and a bigger one – until Jess was covered!

Pat and Julian laughed. Jess was a snow **CAT**!

Postman Pat's Busy Day

Colour in these pictures of my **busy day**. Can you draw a little hand on each of the clocks to show the time?

It's **6 o'clock**.
Time for Pat to get ready.

It's **7 o'clock**.
Time for breakfast.

It's **8 o'clock**. There are lots of letters to deliver.

It's **2 o'clock**. Pat delivers Meera's birthday present.

It's **4 o'clock**. Work is over. The end of another busy day. Goodbye, Pat, Goodbye, Jess!